KEYBC[illegible]S

THE EXAM AT A GLANCE

For your Rock & Pop exam you will need to perform a set of **three songs** and one of the **Session skills** assessments, either **Playback** or **Improvising**. You can choose the order in which you play your set-list.

Song 1

Choose a song from this book

OR from www.trinityrock.com

Song 2

Choose a different song from this book

OR from www.trinityrock.com

OR perform a song you have chosen yourself: this could be your own cover version or a song you have written. It should be at the same level as the songs in this book.

Song 3: Technical focus

Choose one of the Technical focus songs from this book, which cover three specific technical elements.

Session skills

Choose either **Playback** or **Improvising**.

When you are preparing for your exam please check on **www.trinityrock.com** for the most up-to-date information and requirements as these can change from time to time.

CONTENTS

Trinity College London's Rock & Pop syllabus and supporting publications have been devised and produced in association with Faber Music and Peters Edition London.

Trinity College London
Registered office:
89 Albert Embankment
London SE1 7TP UK
T + 44 (0)20 7820 6100
F + 44 (0)20 7820 6161
E music@trinitycollege.co.uk
www.trinitycollege.co.uk

Registered in the UK. Company no. 02683033
Charity no. 1014792
Patron HRH The Duke of Kent KG

First published in 2012 by Trinity College London

Cover and book design by Chloë Alexander
Brand development by Andy Ashburner @ Caffeinehit (www.caffeinehit.com)
Photographs courtesy of Rex Features Limited.
Printed in England by Caligraving Ltd

Audio produced, mixed and mastered by Tom Fleming
Piano and keyboards arranged by Oliver Weeks
Backing tracks arranged by Tom Fleming
Musicians
Vocals: Bo Walton, Brendan Reilly & Alison Symons
Keyboards: Oliver Weeks
Guitar: Tom Fleming
Bass: Ben Hillyard
Drums: George Double
Studio Engineer: Joel Davies www.thelimehouse.com

ISBN: 978-0-85736-240-7

(THEY LONG TO BE) CLOSE TO YOU

The Carpenters
Words by Hal David • Music by Burt Bacharach

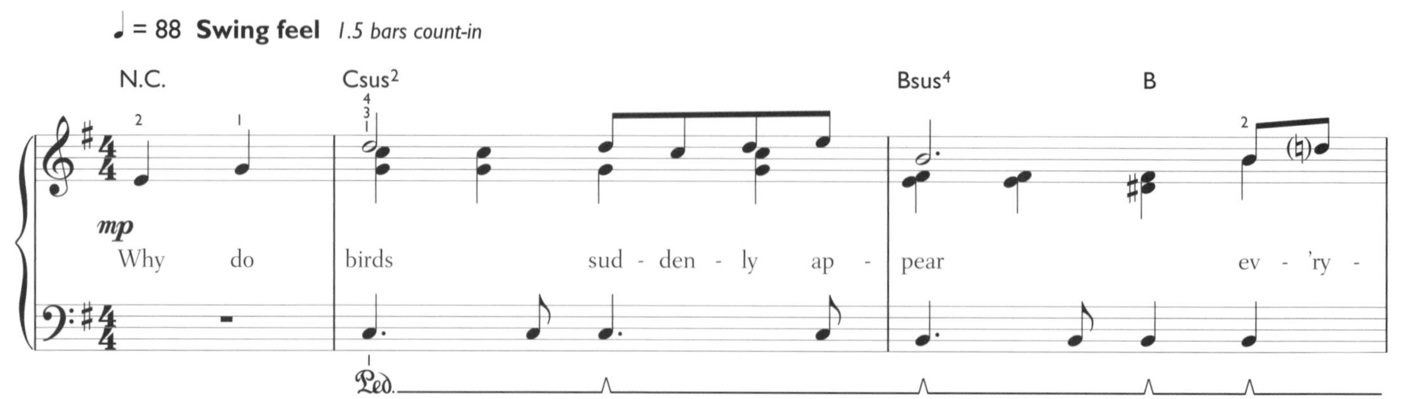

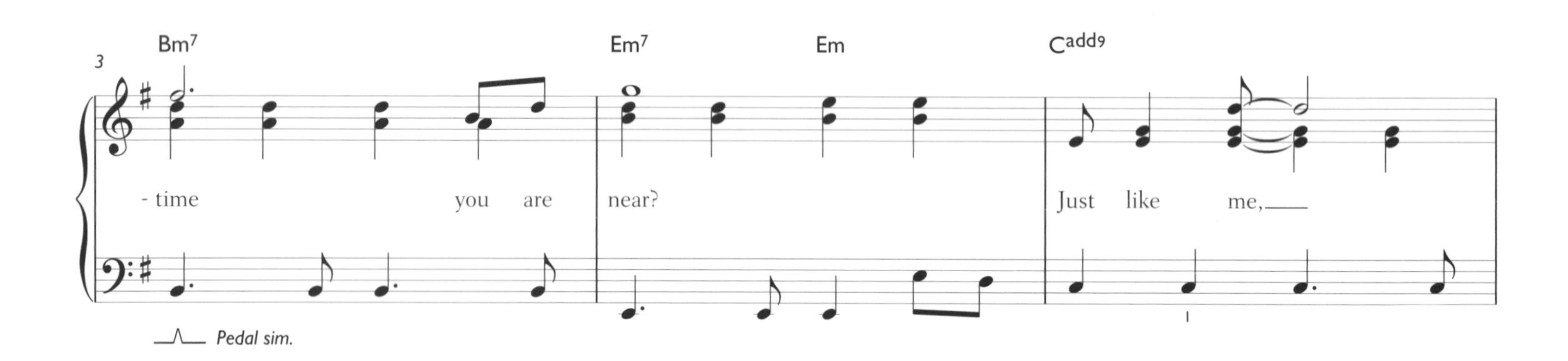

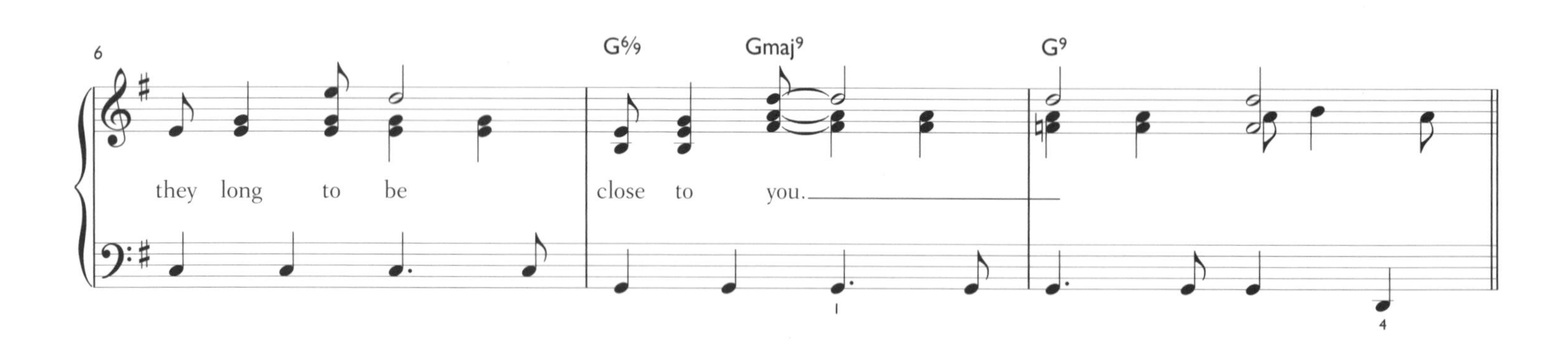

11
Bm7
E11
E9
Cadd9
C
-cid - ed to cre - ate a dream come
true.
So they
sprin-kled moon-dust in your hair of
14
Cmaj7
C6
D
N.C.
gold and star - light in your eyes of
blue.
That is
Ped.
17
Csus2
Bsus4
B
Bm7
why all the girls in
town
fol - low
you all a -
Ped.
Pedal sim.
20
Em7
Em
Cadd9
- round.
Just like me,
22
G6/9
Gmaj9
N.C.
they long to be
close to you.
f

D♭sus2
Csus4
C
Cm7
Fm7
Fm
D♭add9
f (2° mf)
A♭6/9
A♭add9
A♭
optional octaves
mp
Just like me,
rit.
they long to be
p
close to you.

SONGS GET HERE

Oleta Adams
Words and Music by Brenda Russell

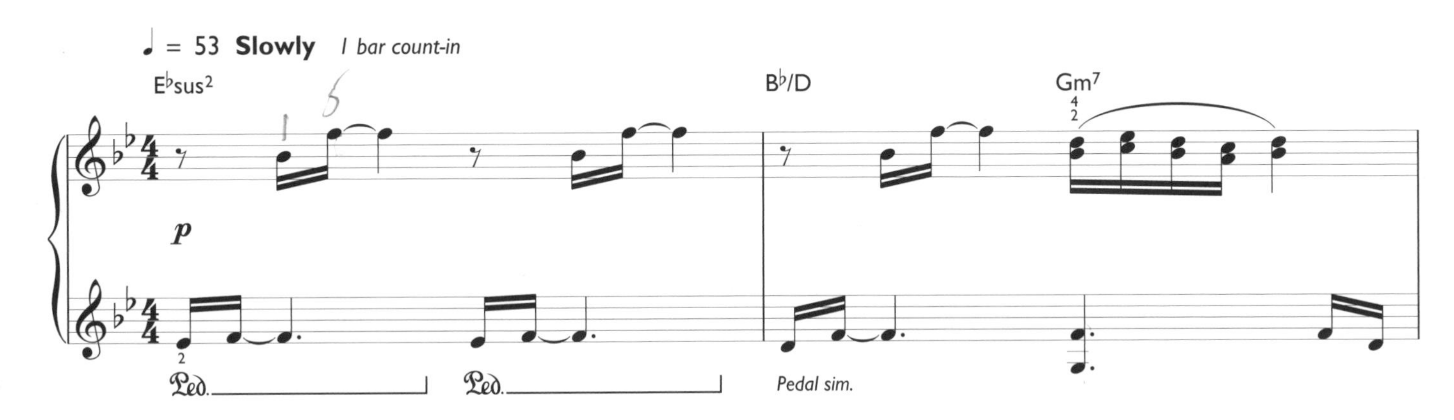

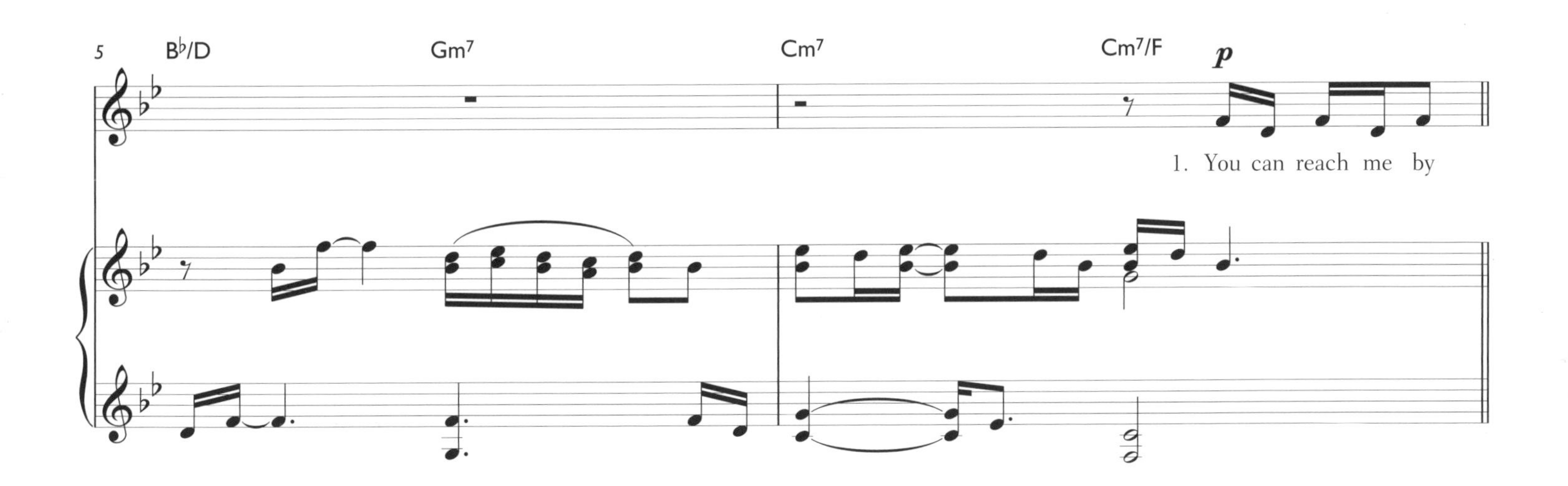

7
E♭sus2
B♭/D
Gm7
rail - way, you can reach me by trail - way. You can reach me on an
9
Cm7
Cm7/F
Gm7
air - plane, you can reach me with your mind. You can reach me by
11
E♭sus2
B♭/D
Gm7
ca - ra - van, cross the des - ert like an a - rab man. I don't care
13
Cm7
Cm7/F
B♭
mp
how you get here, just get here if you can. You can reach me by

15 E♭sus2 B♭/D Gm7
sail - boat, climb a tree and swing rope to rope. Take a sled and slide
mp
17 Cm7 Cm7/F Gm7
down slope in - to these arms of mine. You can jump on a
19 E♭sus2 B♭/D Gm7
speed-y colt, cross the bor-der on a blaze of hope. I don't care
21 Cm7 Cm7/F B♭ A♭/C B♭7/D
how you get here, just get here if you can. There are hills and moun - tains
f

23
E♭maj7
F/E♭
Dm7
be-tween us,
al - ways some thing to get ov - er.
If I

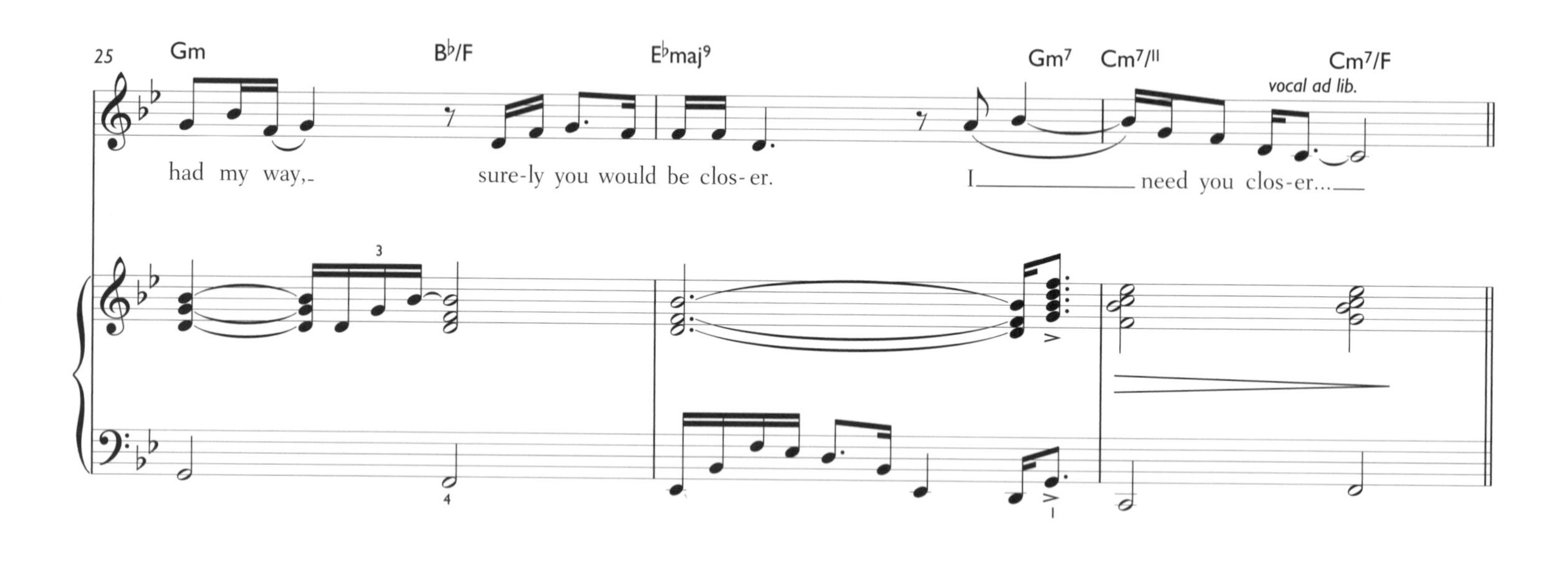
25
Gm
B♭/F
E♭maj9
Gm7
Cm7/II
Cm7/F
vocal ad lib.
had my way,
sure-ly you would be clos- er.
I
need you clos-er...

E♭maj7
KEYBOARD SOLO
28
B♭/D
Gm7
p

30
Cm7
Cm7/F
Gm7
mf

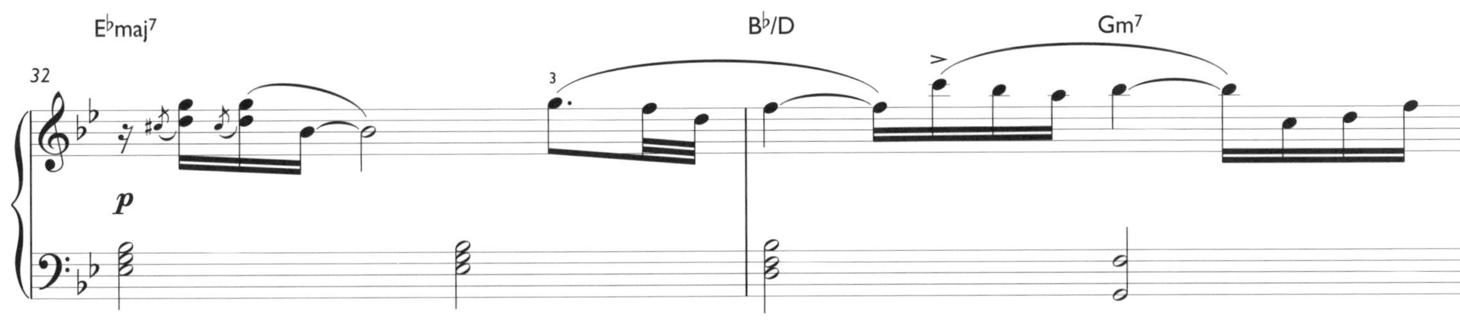
32
E♭maj7
B♭/D
Gm7
p

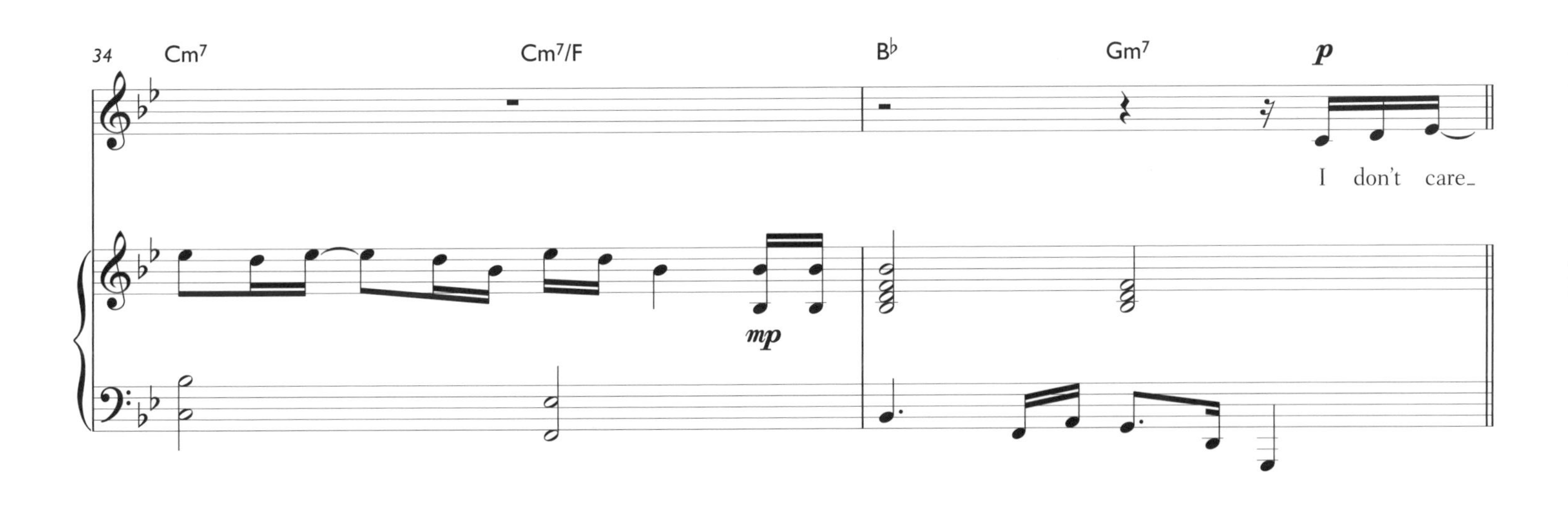
34
Cm7
Cm7/F
B♭
Gm7
p
I don't care
mp

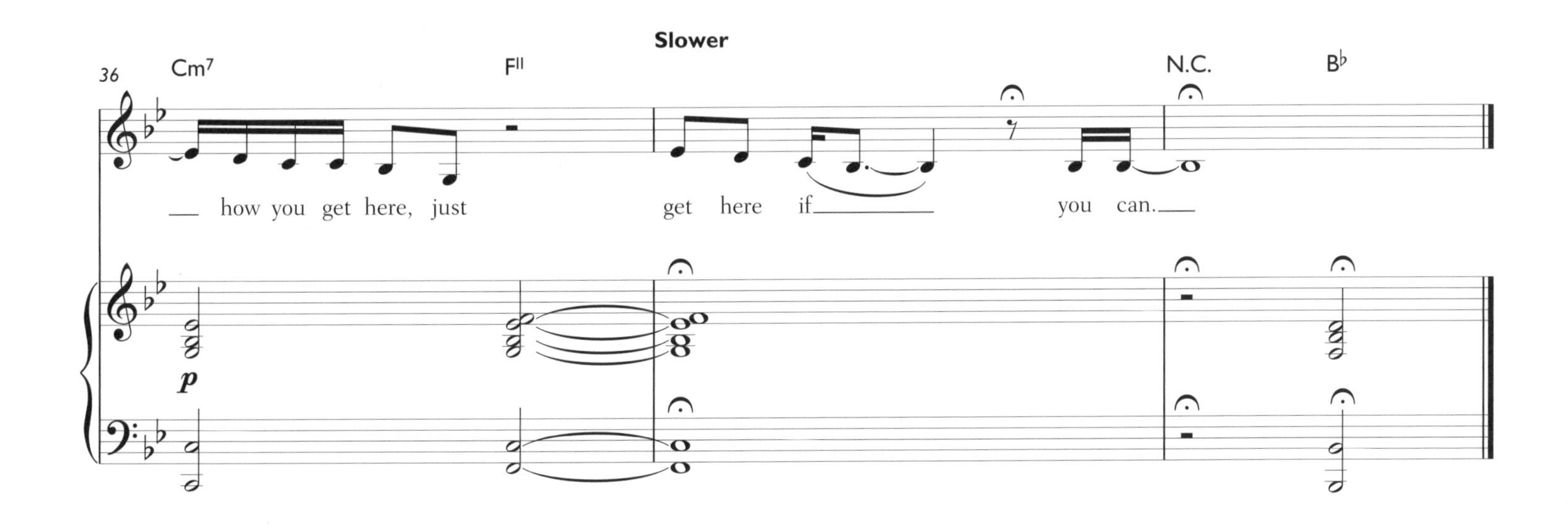
Slower
36
Cm7
F11
N.C.
B♭
how you get here, just get here if you can.
p

demo backing

SONGS I WISH I KNEW HOW IT WOULD FEEL TO BE FREE

Nina Simone

Music by Billy Taylor • Words by Billy Taylor and Dick Dallas

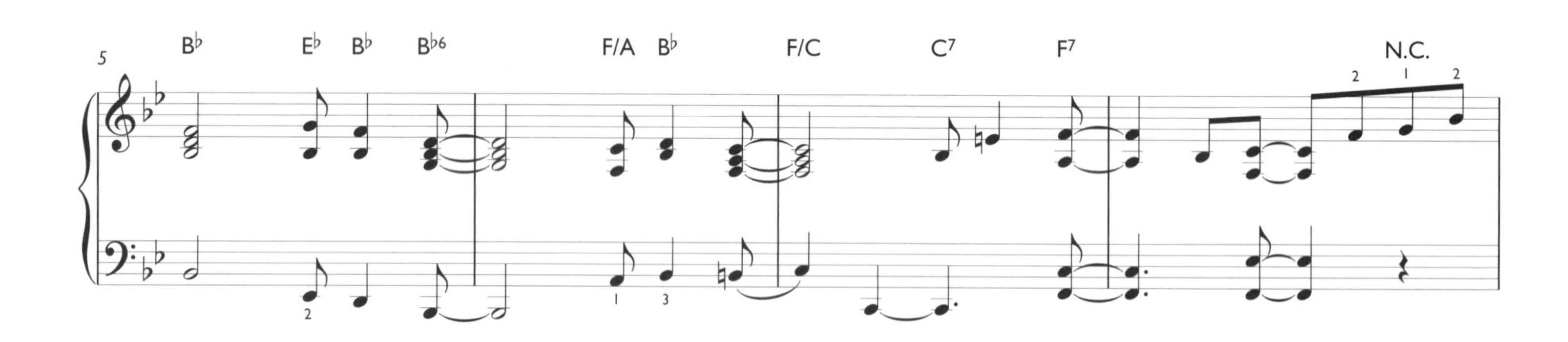

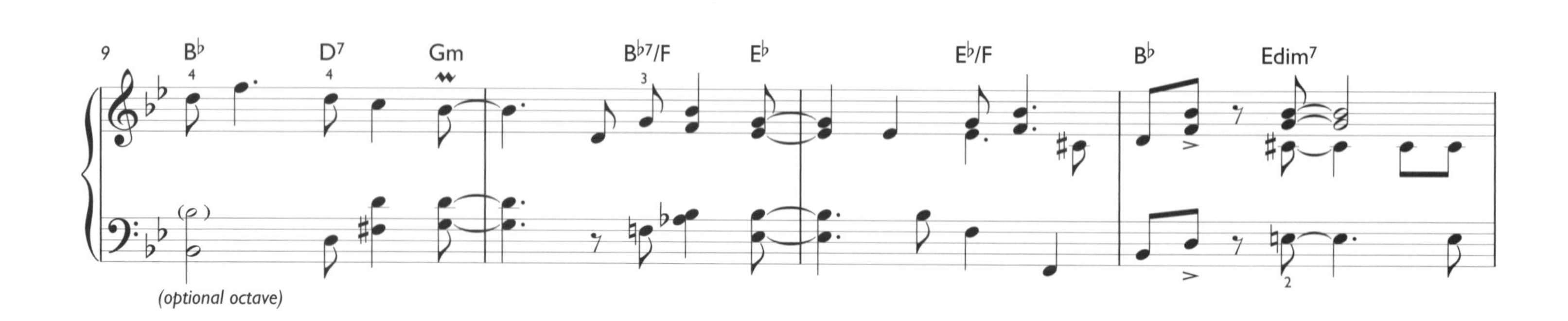

17
B♭ D7/F♯ Gm B♭7/F E♭ E♭/F B♭
wish I knew how it would feel to be free. I
21
B♭ E♭ B♭ F C7 F7
wish I could break all the chains hold - ing me. I
25
Gm/B♭ D7/F♯ Gm B♭7 E♭ E♭/F B♭ Edim7
wish I could say all the things that I should say, say 'em
29
B♭/F D7/F♯ Gm Edim7 B♭/F F7sus4 B♭
loud, say 'em clear, for the whole round world to hear. I
33
D7/F♯ Gm E♭ B♭ E♭/F
mf
wish I could share all the love that's in my heart. Re-

37 B♭ E♭ B♭ F C7 F7
-move all the bars that keep us a - part.
40 B♭ D7/F♯ Gm B♭7
I wish you could know what it means
43 E♭ E♭/F B♭ Gm/E B♭ D7/F♯ Gm
to be me, then you'd see and a - gree
46 Gm/E B♭/F E♭/F B♭
that ev - 'ry man should be free. Well, I
49 B♭ D7/F♯ Gm B♭7 E♭ E♭/F B♭
f
wish I could be like a bird in the sky, how

E♭/F B♭ F C7 F
sweet it would be if I found I could fly. Oh I'd
B♭ D7 Gm B♭7 E♭ E♭/F B♭ Gm/E B♭/F
soar to the sun and look down at the sea. Then I'd sing
D7/F♯ Gm Gm/E B♭/F D7/F♯ Gm
'cause I know yeah, and I'd sing 'cause I know,
E♭ Edim7 B♭/F D7/F♯ Gm E♭ Edim7
yeah! And I'd sing 'cause I know, I know how it
rit.
B♭/F D7/F♯ Gm E♭ Edim7 B♭/F F11 B♭
feels, oh I know how it feels to be free.

BAND OPTION

demo backing

SONGS SCARBOROUGH FAIR

Trad.
Words and Music Trad.

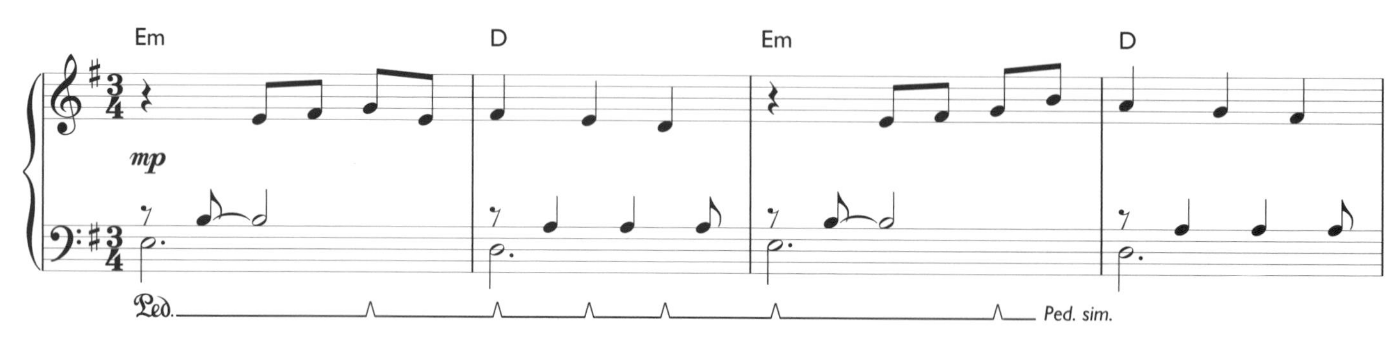

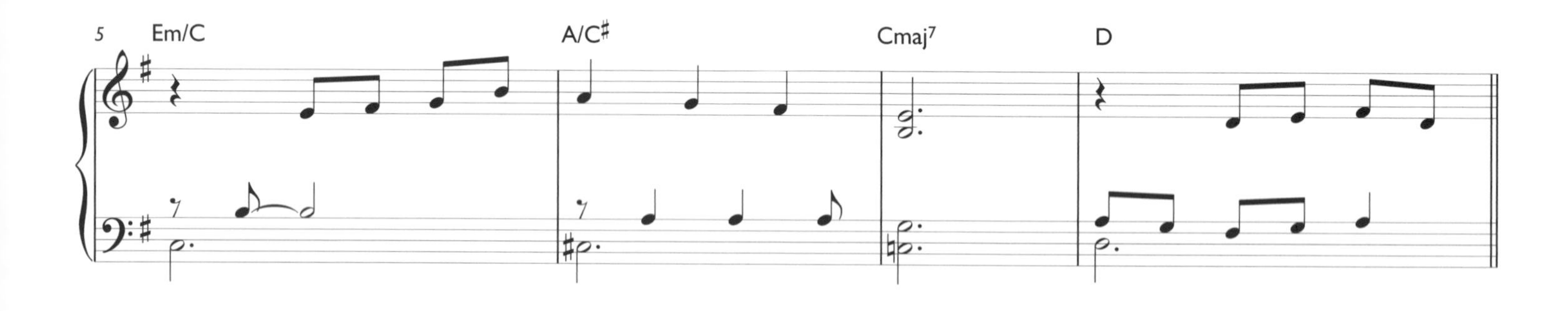

13
G
D/F♯
Em
mf
A
Em
mp
Pars - ley, sage, rose - ma - ry and thyme.
17
mf
G
D/F♯
Em
D
Re - mem - ber me to one who lives there,
mf
22
Em
mp
D
Bm(add4)
she once was a true love of
mp
26
Em
D
Em
D
C
mine.

31
A/C♯
Cmaj7
Dsus2
Em
Tell her to make me a
36
Dsus2
Em
G
D/F♯
Em
A
mf
Camb - ric shirt, pars - ley, sage, rose - ma - ry and
41
Em
mp
mf
G
D/F♯
Em
thyme. With - out a seam or need - le -
46
D
D
Em
mp
D
Bm(add4)
-work, then she'll be a true love of

51
Em
D
Em
D
mine.
55
Cmaj7
A/C♯
Cmaj7
D
59
Em
D
Em
G
p
Tell her to find me an ac - re of land, pars - ley,
64
Em
A
Em
sage, rose - ma - ry and thyme. Be -

68
cresc.
G
D/F♯
Em
D
mf
-tween the salt wa - ter and the sea strand,
mf
72
Em
D
Bm7
p
then she'll be a true love of
p
76
Em
D
Em
D
mine.
mp
80
Cmaj7
A/C♯
Cmaj7
D
Emadd9
p
pp

TECHNICAL FOCUS

HEROES

In your exam, you will be assessed on the following technical elements:

1 Repeated chords and octaves

Playing the first two verses is all about strength and being able to play repeated chords and octaves with an even rhythm and dynamic control. The power here should be in your wrists: you should not find your arms or fingers getting tired. Passages like this are often found in rock and pop music so it is important to build up wrist strength.

2 *Arpeggios*

The *arpeggios* in verse 3 should be delicate and quiet. Make sure they are rhythmical and even – you should be able to hear each note distinctly.

3 Dynamic range

The third verse uses a wide dynamic range, from the opening ***mp***, through a *crescendo* in bars 61–63 to a triumphant ***f*** climax, followed by a quiet ending. Make sure that these differences in dynamics can be heard.

TECHNICAL FOCUS SONGS

BAND OPTION

HEROES

David Bowie

Words by David Bowie • Music by David Bowie and Brian Eno

12 (32)
D
like the dol - phins, like dol-phins can swim.
and you, you will be queen.
15 (35)
G9
C
Though no-thing,
Though no-thing,
18 (38)
D
no-thing can keep us to - ge - ther, we can beat
will tear them a - way, we can be he -
21 (41)
Am
Em
D
them, for - ev - er and ev - er.
- roes, just for one day.

24 (44)
C
G
Oh, we can be he - roes,
Oh, we can be us,
just for one day.
just for one day.
27 (47)
D
D
mp
3. I
I can re -
mp
with sustain pedal
51
Gadd9
G
Dsus2
D
Dsus2
D
- mem - ber
stand - ing
by the
55
Gadd9
G/D
C
mf
wall.
Though no - thing,
mf

58
G
D
Am
nothing can keep us together,
we can beat
61
Em
f
D N.C.
them,
forever and ever.
Oh, we can be he-
f
65
mp C
Gsus2
D
roes,
just for one day.
Oh, we can be he-
mp
69
Am
Em
D
roes,
just for one day.

TECHNICAL FOCUS

KARMA POLICE

In your exam, you will be assessed on the following technical elements:

1 Syncopation

There is a lot of syncopation in the right hand of the verse (bars 9–23) but the left hand has a regular beat, which should help you to play in time. Play this section over and over until it feels and sounds natural. Practise slowly at first, counting eight ♪ beats in a bar and placing the notes carefully. You can then build up the speed as you become more confident.

2 Pedalling

Make sure that you observe the pedal markings and be aware that they are on different beats of the bar. Pedal markings are giving at the beginning of the song: the indication *Pedal sim.* means you should continue pedalling in a similar way. Follow the pedal markings towards the end to avoid the chords blurring and the song sounding muddy.

3 Dynamic range

There should be a contrast between the quiet acoustic beginning of the song and the big, doom-laden section later on. In bars 24–25 there is a *crescendo* followed by a sudden drop from ***f*** to ***p*** and in bars 49–51 there is a *diminuendo* from ***ff*** to ***pp***. Make the most of these dramatic changes.

KARMA POLICE

demo backing

Radiohead

Words and Music by Thomas Yorke, Jonathan Greenwood, Colin Greenwood, Edward O'Brien and Philip Selway

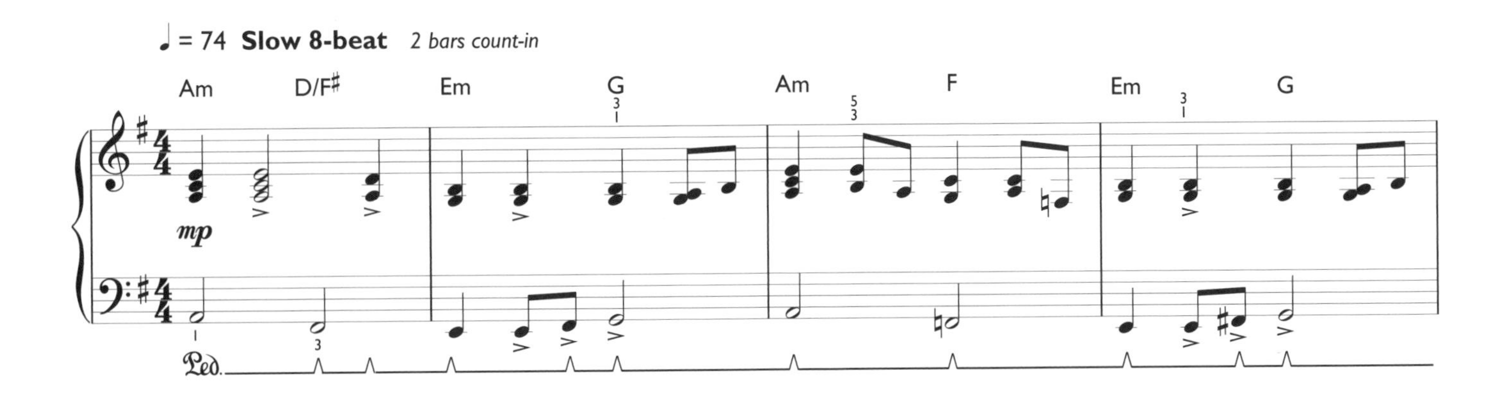

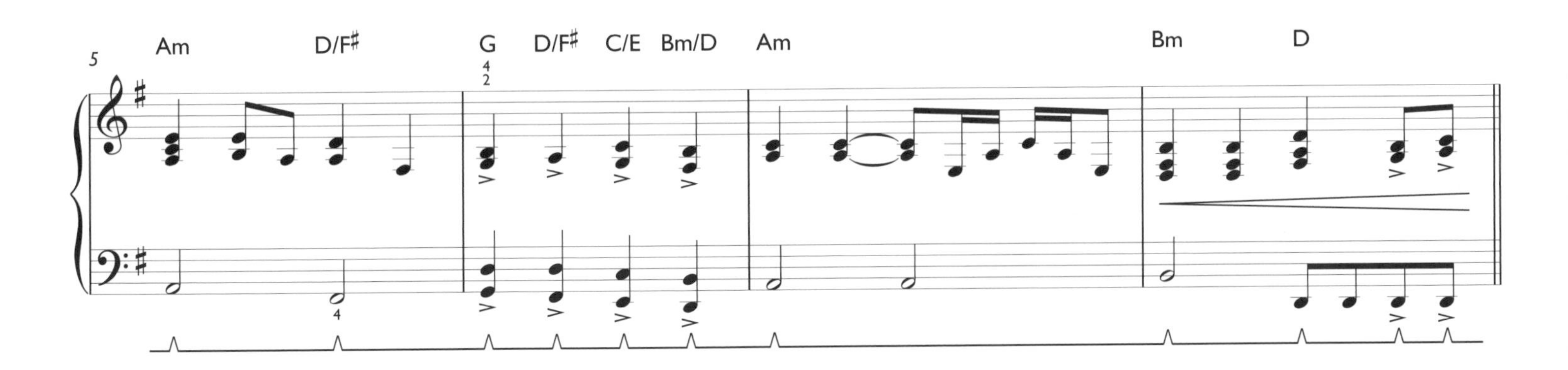

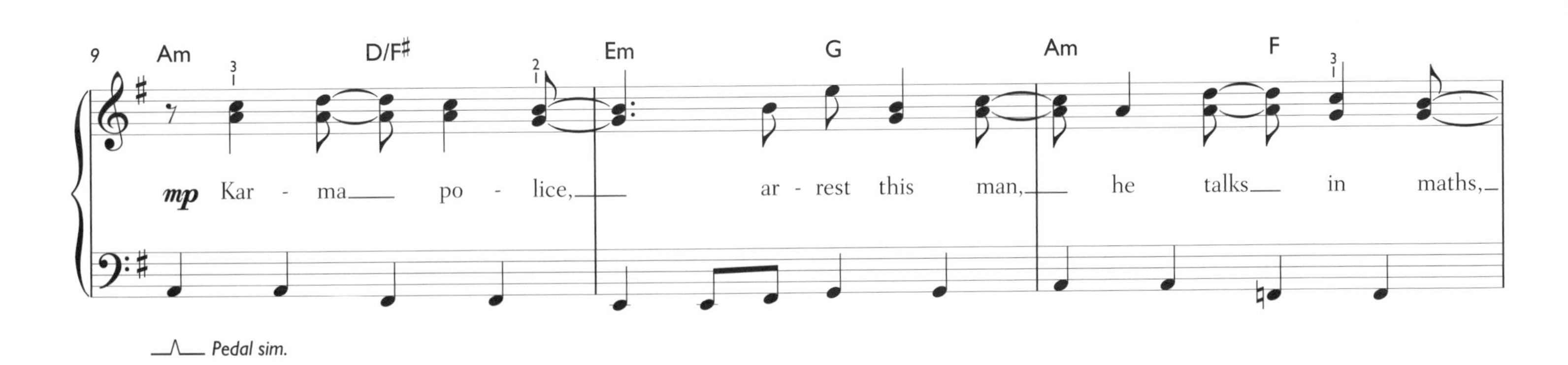

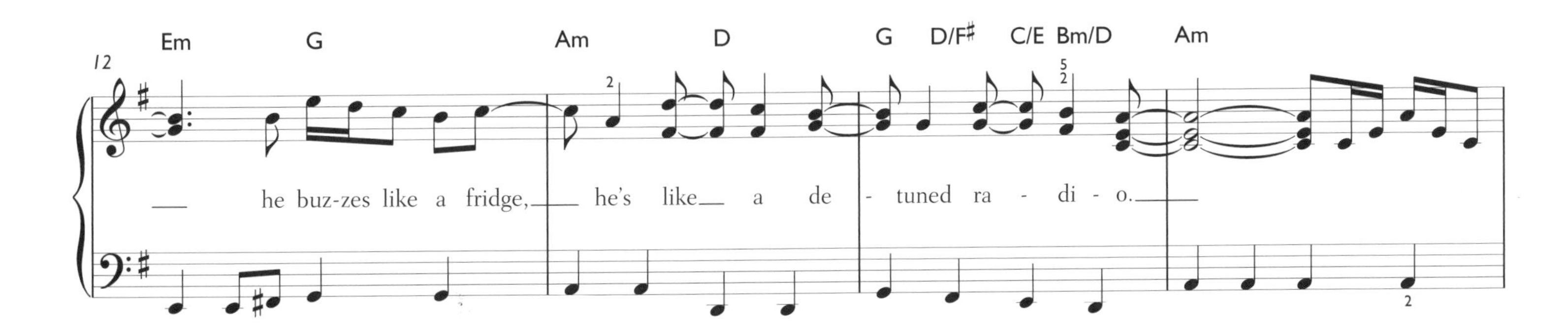

16
Bm
D
Dsus4
D
Am
D/F♯
Em
G
mf Kar - ma po - lice, ar - rest this girl,
19
Am
F
Em
G
Am
D
her Hit - ler hair - do is mak-ing me feel ill, and we have crashed
22
G
D/F♯
C/E
Bm/D
Am
Bm
D
her par - ty.
25
C
D
G
F♯7
C
D
G
F♯7
p This is what you get,
this is what you get,
no pedal
29
C
D
G
Bm
C
Bm/F♯
this is what you get when you mess with us.
f
with pedal

33
Bm
D
G
D
G
D
E
For a min-ute there, I lost my - self, I lost my - self.
37
Bm
D
G
D
G
D
E
Phew, for a min-ute there, I lost my - self, I lost my - self.
41
Bm
D
G
D
G
D
E
E
ff
Pedal sim.
45
Bm
D
G
D
G
D
E9
49
Bm7
pp
Eadd9
E
ppp

ABOUT THE SONGS

(THEY LONG TO BE) CLOSE TO YOU

The Carpenters

The clean-cut brother and sister vocals duo, the Carpenters, came from Los Angeles. Richard Carpenter sang and played keyboards; Karen Carpenter was a skilled drummer but is best remembered for her singing. The sound of the Carpenters was defined by its lush production, precise playing and smooth vocal sound. Karen Carpenter suffered from the eating disorder anorexia nervosa and died at the age of 32 from complications relating to the illness.

'(They Long To Be) Close To You' is the title track of the 1970 album *Close To You*. The song, which went straight to number one, was written by Burt Bacharach and Hal David – a song-writing partnership with a long list of hits since the 1960s. 'Close To You' is Homer and Marge Simpson's love song in the popular television series *The Simpsons*.

'Close To You' is marked 'Swing feel'. This means that for every ♫ you should make the first note longer than the second.

There are many places in this arrangement (bars 1–8, for example) where your right hand has to hold a top note while playing shorter notes, with the same hand, underneath. Make sure that you hold the top note down for its full value.

Practise the syncopated passages (bars 5–7, for example) over and over until they feel and sound natural. Try not to make the chords too heavy. In bars 25 and 32, watch out for the triplets: the three triplet notes should be played in the time normally taken by two.

'Close To You' gets gradually quieter and slower in the final bars. Make sure that these final bars contrast with the loud accented passage before them. The sign on the final chord (⌇) means that the chord should be spread – the notes of the chord should not be played together but one after the other, starting on the beat with the bottom note in the left hand and going quickly upwards.

'They *sprinkled* moondust *in* your *hair* of *gold*'

ABOUT THE SONGS

GET HERE

Oleta Adams

Born in Seattle, USA, Oleta Adams is the daughter of a minister. She began performing in her father's church, and these gospel roots are easily identified in her music. Her big break came when she was discovered by the band Tears For Fears while performing in a Kansas City hotel. They invited her to perform with them on their 1989 album *The Seeds Of Love*: fans were surprised by her soulful vocals.

The following year, Tears For Fears' producer Dave Bascombe produced Oleta Adam's debut album – *Circle Of One* (1990). 'Get Here' is one of the album's stand-out tracks – an aching, gospel-tinged ballad which quickly became an international hit.

'Get Here' has a lovely delicate keyboard part which should flow gently. There is a solo starting at bar 28. Watch out for the triplets and sextuplets in bars 30 and 31. A triplet is a group of three notes played in the time of two, and a sextuplet is basically two consecutive triplets. Make sure that the triplet and sextuplet notes flow evenly.

There are grace notes (also known as 'crushed notes') in bar 32. They are printed in small type next to the main notes. These are very fast notes which should be struck virtually at the same time as the 'main' note. You should be able to hear them clearly but they should not interrupt the flow of the music.

'*You* can *reach* me *with* your *mind*'

ABOUT THE SONGS

I WISH I KNEW HOW IT WOULD FEEL TO BE FREE

Nina Simone

Nina Simone (1933–2003) was an American singer, song-writer, pianist and civil rights activist. She was born – the sixth child of a preacher's family – in North Carolina, USA. A very talented musician, she studied piano at the Julliard School of Music. Although she wished to become the first black concert pianist, she was never able to realise that ambition.

In order to pay for her classical music studies, Nina Simone sang in a bar in Atlantic City, accompanying herself at the piano. It was there that she was first approached by a record company. She created her own distinctive style of music, characterised by its bluesy-jazz feel, powerful emotional singing and elaborate piano parts. She recorded more than 40 albums. 'I Wish I Knew How It Would Feel To Be Free' comes from her 1967 album *Silk & Soul*.

Keep the sound of this song quite dry, using the sustain pedal only later in the song to make the sound a little richer. There should be a slow build-up of dynamics throughout the song, so keep the opening understated and then follow the dynamic markings closely.

There is a lot of syncopation in the song but the left hand often has a straight ♩♩♩♩ pattern (e.g. bar 19), which should help you to play in time and with a steady beat. Enjoy the accented off-beat chord in bar 14 – make it short but heavily accented.

There are several sudden shifts in hand position (in bar 20, for example). Practise these by themselves with a metronome until you are confident about being able to land firmly on the right notes.

'Like a bird in the *sky*'

ABOUT THE SONGS

SCARBOROUGH FAIR

Scarborough Fair was a huge 45-day annual market held in the Yorkshire seaside town of Scarborough. It was internationally famous from the 13th to the 18th centuries, with visitors from all over England and Europe. Some people believe that the herbs in the song – parsley, sage, rosemary and thyme – refer to the plague of the 14th century, when they were used to disguise the smell of the dead or dying. Others believe that the herbs were a love charm.

'Scarborough Fair' is a traditional English ballad and is several hundred years old. Like many folk ballads, it is made up of four-line verses. There are many versions of it and many artists have covered it, most famously Simon and Garfunkel. It was also used as the theme song in the 1967 film *The Graduate*.

'Scarborough Fair' should keep a flowing, waltz-like swing throughout, no matter how complex the keyboard part becomes. Look out for the jumps in the left hand at bar 16 – use the sustain pedal to cover up any gaps in the sound.

In bar 26, both the left and right hands have flowing melodic lines. Practise this section slowly in order to make sure it is clear and well balanced. Take care to observe all the dynamic markings, ending ***pp*** (*pianissimo*) on the final chord.

There are two types of ornament in the song. The first is the mordent (𝆗) in bar 52. This should be played:

=

The second ornament is the *arpeggiation* mark (⦚) on the final chord. This means that the chord should be spread – the notes should be played one after the other, starting on the beat with the bottom note in the left hand, going quickly upwards.

This song is also in the vocals, guitar, bass and drums books, so you can get together and play it in a band.

'*Tell* her *to* find *me* an *acre of* land'

ABOUT THE SONGS

HEROES

David Bowie

'Heroes' – the title track from David Bowie's electronica-influenced album *Heroes* (1977) – was a worldwide hit. Bowie was hugely influential during his peak in the 1970s – effortlessly cool and with an ever-changing image, he achieved cult status, reinventing himself at every turn.

During the late 1970s, Bowie lived in Berlin and worked with ex-Roxy Music member Brian Eno. They experimented with electronic music, producing innovative songs. The synthesiser sounds on this album influenced a whole new generation of bands, including Human League and Gary Numan.

The mood of 'Heroes' is simultaneously both romantic and triumphant. The third verse has a different character to the first two verses: bring out the contrast between this verse and the earlier part of the song. These two parts of the song also require quite different technical skills: the first is dominated by rhythmic ♪ chords; the third verse is much more lyrical and *legato*.

In bars 65, 66, 67 and 70, the chords are *arpeggiated* (⦚). This means that the chords should be spread – the notes of the chord should not be played together but one after the other, starting on the beat with the bottom note in the left hand – and going quickly upwards.

This song is also in the guitar, vocals and bass books, so you can get together and play it in a band.

'*I wish* I could *swim* like *the* dolphins'

ABOUT THE SONGS

KARMA POLICE

Radiohead

'Karma Police' is taken from Radiohead's 1997 album *OK Computer*. The band, whose music is sometimes described as intelligent rock, is not afraid to experiment and takes influences not just from rock music, but also from contemporary classical, jazz, electronic and film music.

OK Computer is a sophisticated album, with subtle rhythms, complex syncopations, and distorted guitars all helping to create unusual textures and atmospheres, not least in 'Karma Police'.

The opening eight bars have several accents, often on off-beats. Make sure that you emphasise these notes – they give rhythmic character to the opening.

The verse and chorus are quite different – in terms of melody, chords and dynamics. Bring out the contrasts between the two sections. The dynamics, in particular, are important throughout the song.

'This is what you get when you mess with us'

SESSION SKILLS

PLAYBACK

For your exam, you can choose either Playback or Improvising (see page 38). If you choose Playback, you will be asked to play some music you have not seen or heard before.

In the exam, you will be given the song chart and the examiner will play a recording of the music on CD. You will hear several two-bar or four-bar phrases on the CD: you should play each of them straight back in turn. There's a rhythm track going throughout, which helps you keep in time. There should not be any gaps in the music.

In the exam you will have two chances to play with the CD:

- First time – for practice
- Second time – for assessment.

You should listen to the audio, copying what you hear; you can also read the music. Here are some practice song charts which are also on the CD in this book.

Practice playback 1

Practice playback 2

'I really *like* the *way* music *looks* on *paper*. It *looks* like *art* to *me*'

Steve Vai

SESSION SKILLS

IMPROVISING

For your exam, you can choose either Playback (see page 36), or Improvising. If you choose to improvise, you will be asked to improvise over a backing track that you haven't heard before in a specified style.

In the exam, you will be given a song chart and the examiner will play a recording of the backing track on CD. The backing track consists of a passage of music played on a loop. You can choose whether to play a lead melodic line, rhythmic chords, or a combination of the two.

In the exam you will have two chances to play with the CD:

- First time – for practice
- Second time – for assessment.

Here are some improvising charts for practice which are also on the CD in this book.

Practice improvisation 1

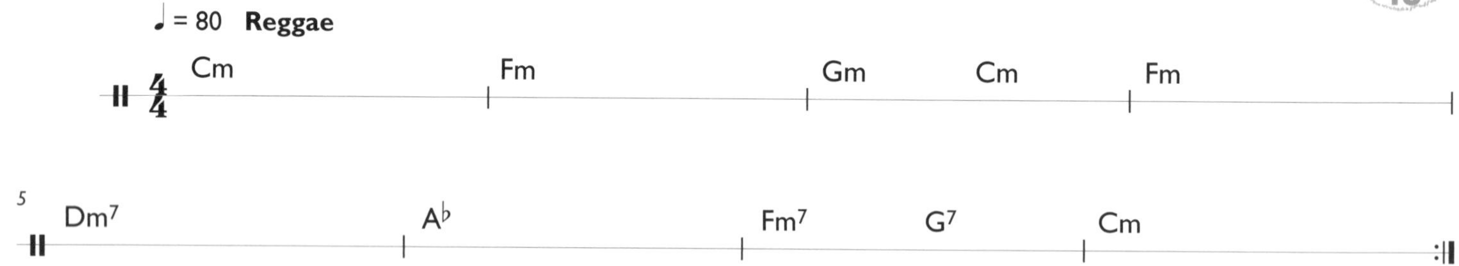

Practice improvisation 2

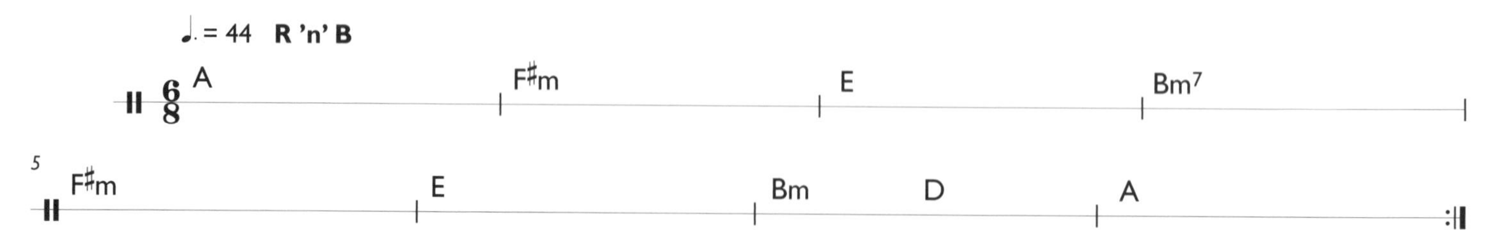

CHOOSING A SONG FOR YOUR EXAM

There are lots of options to help you choose your three songs for the exam. For Songs 1 and 2, you can choose a song which is:

- from this book
- from www.trinityrock.com

Or for Song 2 you can choose a song which is:

- sheet music from a printed or online source
- your own arrangement of a song or a song you have written yourself (see page 40).

You can play the song unaccompanied or with a backing track (minus the solo instrument). If you like, you can create a backing track yourself (or with friends), or you could add your own vocals – or both.

For Grade 4, the song should last between two and three-and-a-half minutes, and the level of difficulty should be similar to your other songs. When choosing a song, think about:

- Does it work on my instrument?
- Are there any technical elements that are too difficult for me? (If so, perhaps save it for when you do the next grade.)
- Do I enjoy playing it?
- Does it work with my other pieces to create a good set-list?

SHEET MUSIC

You must always bring an original copy of the book or a download sheet with email certificate for each song you perform in the exam. If you choose to write your own song you must provide the examiner with a copy of the sheet music. Your music can be:

- a lead sheet with lyrics, chords and melody line
- a chord chart with lyrics
- a full score using conventional staff notation
- see page 40 for details on presenting a song you have written yourself.

The title of the song and your name should be on the sheet music.

HELP PAGES

WRITING YOUR OWN SONG

You can play a song that you have written yourself for one of the choices in your exam. For Grade 4, your song should last between two and three-and-a-half minutes. It is sometimes difficult to know where to begin, however. Here are some suggestions for starting points:

- **A rhythm**: A short repeated rhythm will often underpin an entire song. Start by writing a couple of short rhythms here:

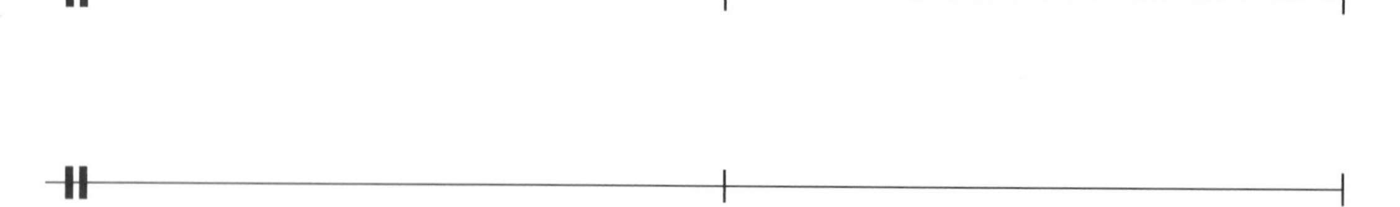

- **Lyrics**: You could start by writing lyrics, or choosing someone else's lyrics (be aware of the copyright issues if you do this – see page 42 for further details). Your lyrics will help you decide whether your song will be upbeat or reflective, and may help you decide on a style and structure.

- **Style**: What style will your song be in? Try out some different rock and pop styles – such as blues, hard rock, bhangra or pop.

There are plenty of other ways of starting: perhaps with a riff or a chord sequence, for example.

You will also need to consider the **structure** of your song (verse and chorus, 12-bar blues, and so on) and what **instruments** it is for (solo keyboards or voice/keyboards/drums . . .).

There are many choices to be made – which is why writing a song is such a rewarding thing to do.

WRITING YOUR SONG DOWN

Rock and pop music is often written as a **lead sheet** with the lyrics (if there are any), chords and a melody line.

- As a keyboards player, you may want to write your complete part on **two staves**, as has been used for the songs in this book.
- You can, if you prefer, use a **graph** or **table** to represent your music, as long as it is clear to anyone else (including the examiner) how the song goes.

HELP PAGES

PLAYING IN A BAND

Playing in a band is exciting: it can be a lot of fun and, as with everything, the more you do it, the easier it gets. It is very different from playing on your own. Everyone contributes to the overall sound: the most important skill you need to develop is listening.

For a band to sound good, the players need to be 'together' – that mainly means keeping in time with each other, but also playing at the same volume, and with the same kind of feeling.

Your relationship with the other band members is also important. Talk with them about the music you play, the music you like, and what you'd like the band to achieve short-term and long-term.

Band rehearsals are important – you should not be late, tired or distracted by your mobile phone! Being positive makes a huge difference. Try to create a friendly atmosphere in rehearsals so that everybody feels comfortable trying out new things. Don't worry about making mistakes: that is what rehearsals are for.

'Scarborough Fair' on page 16 and 'Heroes' on page 22 are arranged for band: you will find parts for vocals, guitar, bass and drums ('Scarborough Fair' only) in the other Trinity Rock & Pop Grade 4 books or available online. Trinity offers exams for groups of musicians at various levels. The songs arranged for bands are ideal to include as part of a set-list for these exams. Have a look at the website for more details.

HINTS AND TIPS

- Discuss with the other band members how you want to play each song. Decide whether to have instrumental solos or improvised fills – variety helps keep your performance interesting. Make sure that you all know what each member of the band is going to do and when – this will make a professional performance.

- Even when you are playing in a band, it is important to do individual practice. Work on all of your part – the sections where you are not playing a prominent role are just as important as when you are playing a solo. If all the band members can play their parts well, the overall performance is much more likely to be slick and rhythmically tight.

- Nothing beats the thrill of performing live in front of an audience. Organise a gig for a few friends. It can be a small gig in someone's house – the important thing is to get used to playing in front of other people. Gigs can be nerve-wracking at first, but try to relax and enjoy them.

HELP PAGES

PLAYING WITH BACKING TRACKS

The CD contains demos and backing tracks of all the songs in the book. The additional songs at www.trinityrock.com also come with demos and backing tracks.

- In your exam, you should perform with the backing track, or you can create your own (see below).
- Keyboard players should not use auto-accompaniment features for these exams as the aim is to play with a backing track.
- The backing tracks begin with a click track, which sets the tempo and helps you start accurately.
- Be careful to set the balance between the volume of the backing track and your instrument.
- Listen carefully to the backing track to ensure you are playing in time.

If you are creating your own backing track here are some further tips:

- Make sure the sound quality is of a good standard.
- Think carefully about the instruments/sounds you are putting on the backing track.
- Avoid copying what you are playing on the backing track – it should support not duplicate.
- Do you need to include a click track at the beginning?

COPYRIGHT IN A SONG

If you are a singer or songwriter it is important to know about copyright. When someone writes a song or creates an arrangement they own the copyright (sometimes called 'the rights') to that version. The copyright means that other people cannot copy it, sell it, perform it in a concert, make it available online or record it without the owner's permission or the appropriate licence. When you write a song you automatically own the copyright to it, which means that other people cannot copy your work. But, just as importantly, you cannot copy other people's work, or perform it in public without their permission or the appropriate licence.

Points to remember

- You can create a cover version of a song and play it in an exam or other non-public performance.
- You cannot record your cover version and make your recording available to others (by copying it or uploading it to a website) without the appropriate licence.
- You do own the copyright of your own original song, which means that no one is allowed to copy it.
- You cannot copy someone else's song without their permission or the appropriate licence.

YOUR PAGE NOTES

ALSO AVAILABLE

Trinity College London Rock & Pop examinations 2012-2017 are also available for:

Bass Initial
ISBN: 978-0-85736-227-8

Bass Grade 1
ISBN: 978-0-85736-228-5

Bass Grade 2
ISBN: 978-0-85736-229-2

Bass Grade 3
ISBN: 978-0-85736-230-8

Bass Grade 4
ISBN: 978-0-85736-231-5

Bass Grade 5
ISBN: 978-0-85736-232-2

Bass Grade 6
ISBN: 978-0-85736-233-9

Bass Grade 7
ISBN: 978-0-85736-234-6

Bass Grade 8
ISBN: 978-0-85736-235-3

Drums Initial
ISBN: 978-0-85736-245-2

Drums Grade 1
ISBN: 978-0-85736-246-9

Drums Grade 2
ISBN: 978-0-85736-247-6

Drums Grade 3
ISBN: 978-0-85736-248-3

Drums Grade 4
ISBN: 978-0-85736-249-0

Drums Grade 5
ISBN: 978-0-85736-250-6

Drums Grade 6
ISBN: 978-0-85736-251-3

Drums Grade 7
ISBN: 978-0-85736-252-0

Drums Grade 8
ISBN: 978-0-85736-253-7

Guitar Initial
ISBN: 978-0-85736-218-6

Guitar Grade 1
ISBN: 978-0-85736-219-3

Guitar Grade 2
ISBN: 978-0-85736-220-9

Guitar Grade 3
ISBN: 978-0-85736-221-6

Guitar Grade 4
ISBN: 978-0-85736-222-3

Guitar Grade 5
ISBN: 978-0-85736-223-0

Guitar Grade 6
ISBN: 978-0-85736-224-7

Guitar Grade 7
ISBN: 978-0-85736-225-4

Guitar Grade 8
ISBN: 978-0-85736-226-1

Keyboards Initial
ISBN: 978-0-85736-236-0

Keyboards Grade 1
ISBN: 978-0-85736-237-7

Keyboards Grade 2
ISBN: 978-0-85736-238-4

Keyboards Grade 3
ISBN: 978-0-85736-239-1

Keyboards Grade 4
ISBN: 978-0-85736-240-7

Keyboards Grade 5
ISBN: 978-0-85736-241-4

Keyboards Grade 6
ISBN: 978-0-85736-242-1

Keyboards Grade 7
ISBN: 978-0-85736-243-8

Keyboards Grade 8
ISBN: 978-0-85736-244-5

Vocals Initial
ISBN: 978-0-85736-254-4

Vocals Grade 1
ISBN: 978-0-85736-255-1

Vocals Grade 2
ISBN: 978-0-85736-256-8

Vocals Grade 3
ISBN: 978-0-85736-257-5

Vocals Grade 4
ISBN: 978-0-85736-258-2

Vocals Grade 5
ISBN: 978-0-85736-259-9

Vocals Grade 6 (female voice)
ISBN: 978-0-85736-263-6

Vocals Grade 6 (male voice)
ISBN: 978-0-85736-260-5

Vocals Grade 7 (female voice)
ISBN: 978-0-85736-264-3

Vocals Grade 7 (male voice)
ISBN: 978-0-85736-261-2

Vocals Grade 8 (female voice)
ISBN: 978-0-85736-265-0

Vocals Grade 8 (male voice)
ISBN: 978-0-85736-262-9

E♭sus2
B♭/D
Gm7
rail - way, you can reach me by trail - way. You can reach me on an
Cm7
Cm7/F
Gm7
air - plane, you can reach me with your mind. You can reach me by
11
E♭sus2
B♭/D
Gm7
ca - ra - van, cross the des - ert like an a - rab man. I don't care
13
Cm7
Cm7/F
B♭
mp
how you get here, just get here if you can. You can reach me by